THE SNOW QUEEN

a musical play in two acts

Book and Lyrics by
WINIFRED PALMER

Based on the story by
HANS ANDERSEN

Musical Score adapted by
KING PALMER

From the music of
EDVARD GRIEG

Josef Weinberger Ltd.
10-16, Rathbone St., London, W1P 2BJ
telephone 01-580 2827

SYNOPSIS OF SCENES

ACT I	PROLOGUE	Tabs.
	SCENE 1	Interior: Karl and Gerda's Home.
	SCENE 2	Tabs: On the Way to the Snow Queen's Palace.
	SCENE 3	The Magic Flower Garden.
	SCENE 4	The Royal Palace.
ACT II	SCENE 1	The Robber Camp.
	SCENE 2	Interior: The Finnish Woman's Hut.
	SCENE 3	The Snow Queen's Palace.
	SCENE 4	Interior: Karl and Gerda's Home.

THE ACTION TAKES PLACE IN SCANDINAVIA OVER
A PERIOD OF WINTER MONTHS.

MUSIC PLOT

ACT I

1. Prelude.

SCENE 1.

2. 'One Day in a Merry Mood' .... The Hobgoblin
3. 'Winter' .... Karl, Gerda and Grandmother
4. 'The Snow Queen' .... Grandmother
5. 'Ugly' .... Karl
6. 'I'll Follow' .... Gerda, Grandmother, Hans and Lars

SCENE 2.

7. 'Come' .... The Snow Queen

SCENE 3.

8. 'The Flower Garden' .... Soldiers and Flowers
9. 'Flower Song' .... Gerda and Flowers

SCENE 4.

10. Dance .... Courtiers
11. 'For Ever' .... Prince, Princess and Chorus
12. 'Crows in Clover' .... Two Crows
13. Reprise: 'For Ever' .... Prince, Princess and Chorus

ACT II

SCENE 1.

14. 'We Ride Over the Mountains' .... Robber King and Robber Band
15. Reprise: 'We Ride Over the Mountains' .... Robber King and Robber Band
16. 'Far Away' .... Reindeer, Gerda and Robber Girl
17. Reprise: 'We Ride Over the Mountains' .... Robber King and Robber Band
18. Reprise: 'We Ride Over the Mountains' .... (Played only)

SCENE 2.

19. 'Fish' .... Finnish Woman
20. 'Innocence' .... Finnish Woman

SCENE 3.

21. Ballet of Snowflakes (optional)
22. 'Words' .... Karl and The Snow Queen
23. Reprise: 'Winter' .... Gerda
24. 'Home' .... Karl and Gerda
25. 'One That Got Away' .... The Hobgoblin

SCENE 4.

26. Reprise: 'Home' .... Karl, Gerda, Grandmother and Children

CAST

SINGING CHARACTERS

THE HOBGOBLIN	A wicked, spindly character of black magic arts.	
KARL	A lively boy of about twelve years.	
GERDA	His sister, a pretty girl a year or so his junior.	
GRANDMOTHER	A very comfortable-looking old lady.	
HANS LARS	Two boys of about Karl's age.	
THE SNOW QUEEN	Tall and coldly beautiful.	
PRINCE PRINCESS	A handsome couple, newly married and very happy.	
TWO CROWS	Very loquacious birds.	

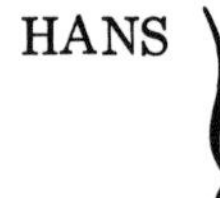

THE ROBBER KING A handsome villain.

THE ROBBER GIRL Dark, fierce and dashing.

THE REINDEER A haughty animal.

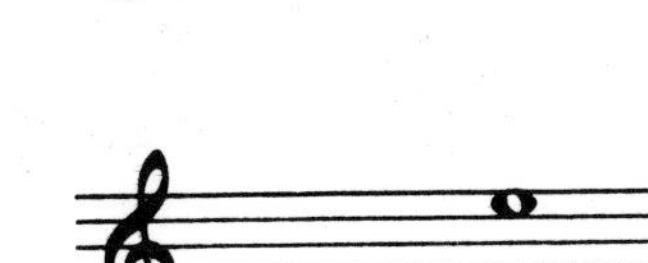

THE FINNISH WOMAN A practical, kindly woman.

NON-SINGING CHARACTERS

THE OLD WOMAN A little rosy-apple of a woman who has a magic garden.

COURT CHAMBERLAIN

THE OLD ROBBER WOMAN An ugly, vile old woman.

CHORUS

SOLDIERS, FLOWERS, COURTIERS, ROBBER BAND, SNOWFLAKES, CHILDREN,

(N.B. The music for the chorus which is arranged in two parts:

voice ranges

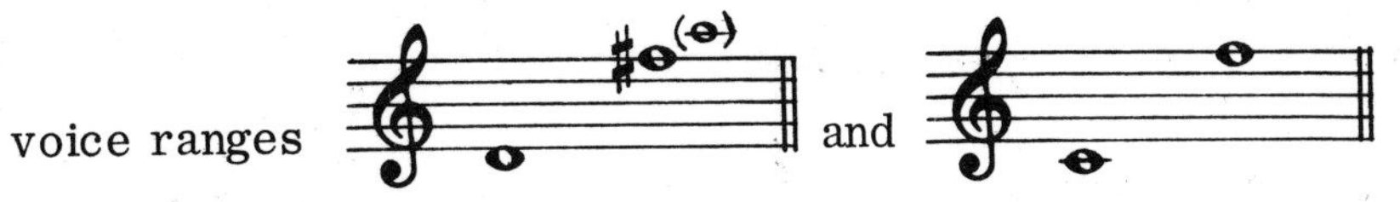

may be sung in unison if desired.)

THE SNOW QUEEN

Book and Lyrics by WINIFRED PALMER
Based on the story by HANS ANDERSEN

Musical score adapted by KING PALMER
From the music of EDVARD GRIEG

1. PRELUDE

2 **Allegretto**

poco rit.
3
a tempo
4 Andante espressivo
f
rit.
SEGUE No. 2

2. ONE DAY IN A MERRY MOOD

THE HOBGOBLIN

1
Alla marcia
One day in a mer-ry mood, Hating all that is good,
p
sempre stacc.
I made such a look-ing glass as you have ne-ver seen. Ev-ery-one re-flected there
had no nose, had no hair, Seemed to stand up-on their heads, their teeth were dir-ty green.
Faults be-came a gi-ant size, In the poor viewer's eyes. Virtues shrank to no-thing but

2
lit-tle pin heads. But the mir-ror broke and flew up on high in the blue,
Splin-ters float - ed in the air, shat-tered in shreds. Should a piece get in your eye,
that is the rea-son why You will see the world as such an ug-ly place to be.
3
And if one fine silvery dart finds its way to your heart, It will freeze, and now you see that

3. WINTER

(KARL AND GERDA AND GRANDMOTHER)

frosty window pane, And you see the snowy world again.
5
Karl and Gerda
Cold, cold, Winter cold, Shivering with falling snow
Old, old, Winter old. When will cruel winter go?
6
Gerda
Will the Springtime soon be here? Will the
window soon be clear so that we can see at last That the cruel Winter's
fz

7
Karl and Gerda
reign is past?—
Cold, cold,— Win-ter cold,—— Shiv-er-ing with fal-ling
Old, old,—— Win-ter old.——— When will cru-el win-ter
snow.
go?
8
Karl, Gerda and Grandmother
Make the big brown pen-nies
hot. Take one up, find a spot On the fros-ty win-dow
pane, And you see the snow-y world a-gain.——
fz
poco rit.

DIALOGUE

CUE: Grandmother: "Sit down both of you and listen".

4. THE SNOW QUEEN

(GRANDMOTHER)

Andante espressivo

p

Up in the sky where the snowflakes swarm and fly Su-

preme reigns the Snow Queen. North in the land with the ice on every hand, A-

lone reigns the Snow Queen.

1

Still and a-lone on her

i-cy royal throne, Re-splen - dent and cold. Scorn-ing the sun, she will

2
wait until it's done, And sum - mer is old. Out then she flies, rising
mf
mp

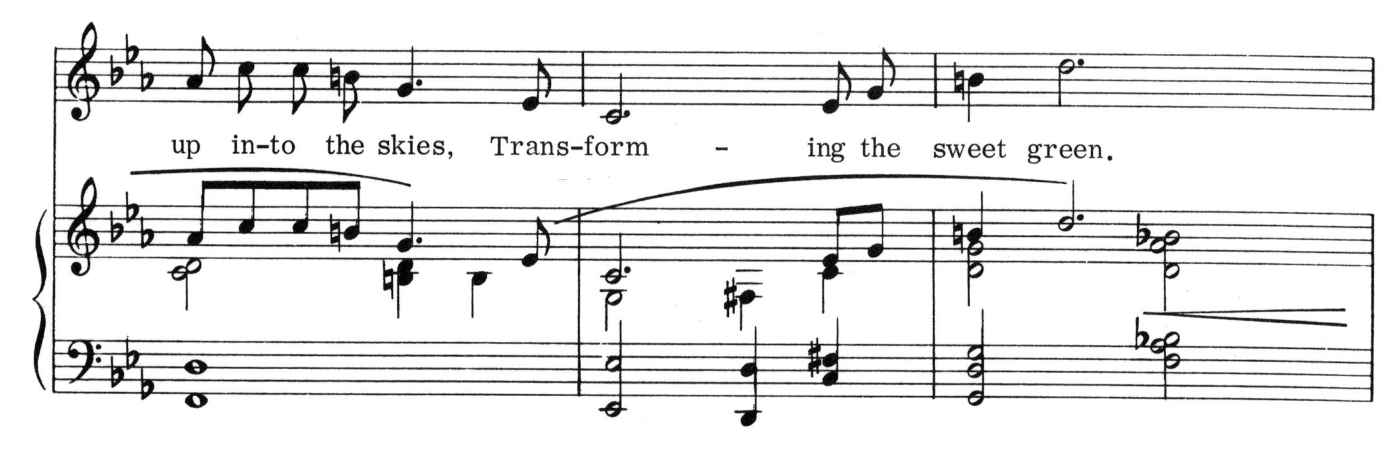
up in-to the skies, Trans-form - ing the sweet green.

Now all is white, where she travels through the night. Ah, yes, that's the
f
p

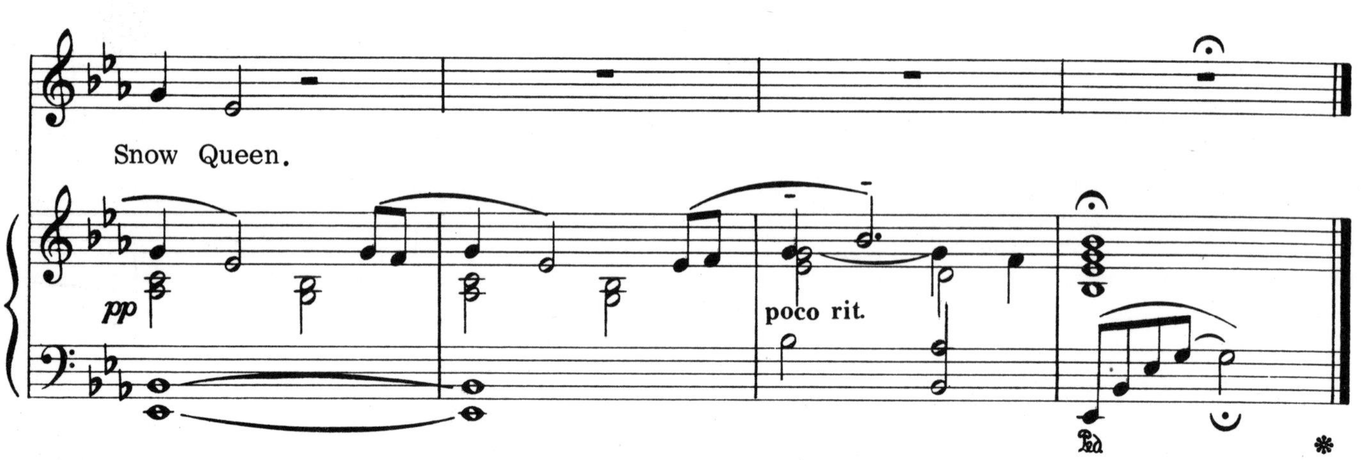
Snow Queen.
pp
poco rit.
Dialogue

CUE: Karl: "You're even uglier when you cry".

5. UGLY

(KARL)

2
ug-li-ness is just you!
When you cry your face is just like thun -
mp
f

- der.
Oh, what a sight!
You look a fright.
fp
fp

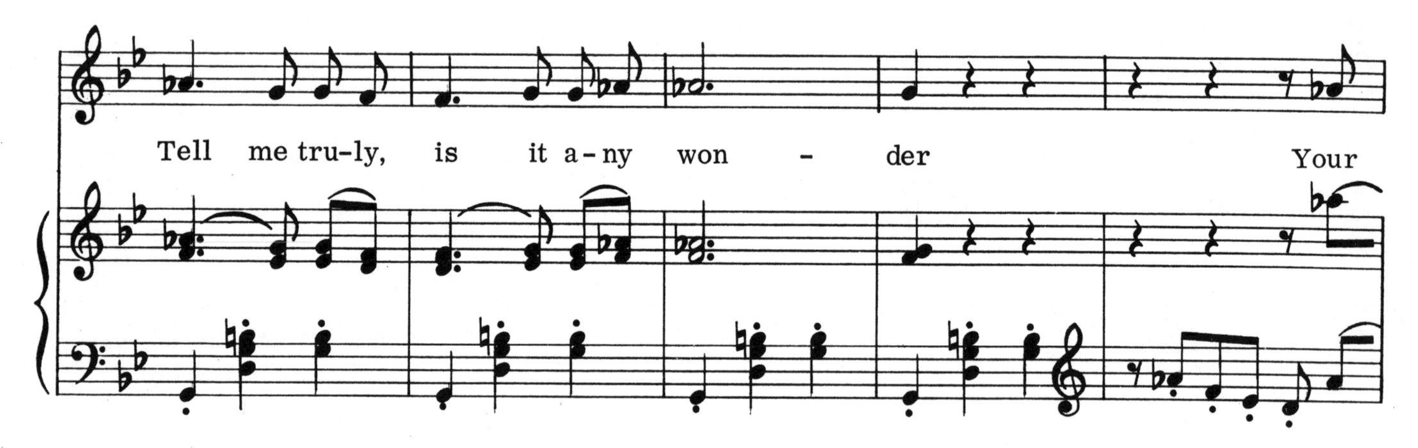
Tell me tru-ly, is it a-ny won - der
Your

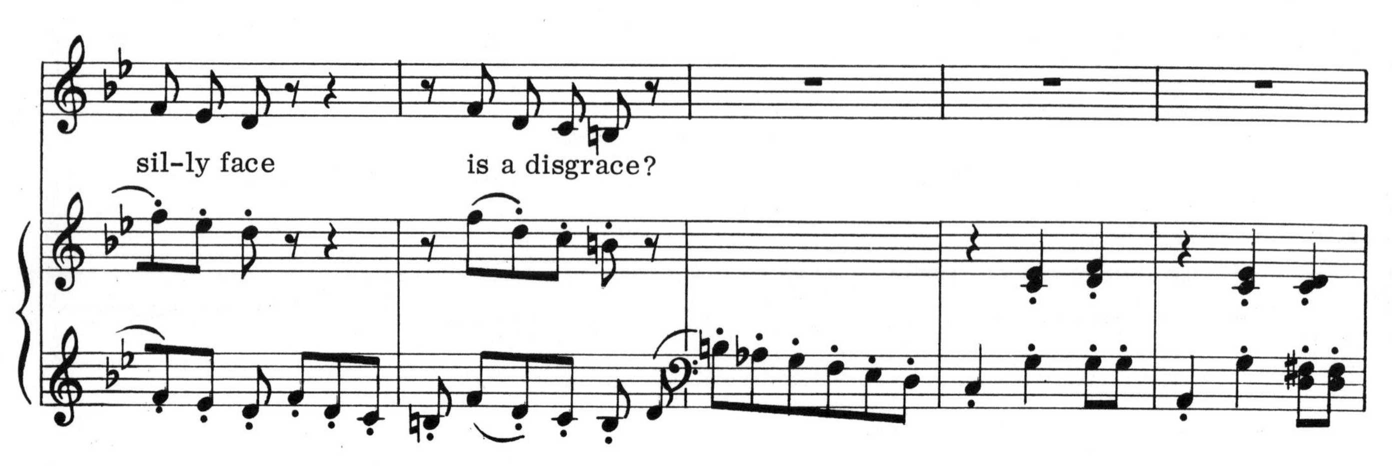
sil-ly face is a disgrace?

3
You fancy you're a ver-y graceful child, And dainty in your ways. Ug-ly is the word for you, clumsy and ga - lumphing too.
4
Stupid, a-sinine, brainless and bovine, sil-ly and porcine, foolish and feline;
They're the very words that so describe you, In fact, ug-liness is just you!
p
f
tr

Dialogue

CUE. Gerda: "You understand that, don't you". Grandmother: "I understand, my dear".

6. I'LL FOLLOW

(GERDA, GRANDMOTHER, HANS AND LARS)

Hans & Lars
cold, — shiv - er - ing with fal - ling snow. Old, old, — Win - ter
old. — When will cru - el win - ter go?
Gerda
2
When the Spring flowers come a - gain, When the birds greet the
rain, When the world is bright and new We will come back home a -
fz

3 Andante
All
-gain to you.
Though every
step is long, I'll take it light - ly.
And e - ven though the
road be hard I'll fol - low him to all e - ter - ni - ty,
I'll fol - low him to all e -
- ter - ni - ty.
fz
ritard.
a tempo
dim.
Music continues (D.C.) quietly until:
Snow Queen: "We have done well, little Karl".
Dialogue

7. COME

(SNOW QUEEN)

Snow Queen: "You will learn to live when you reach my palace, come.

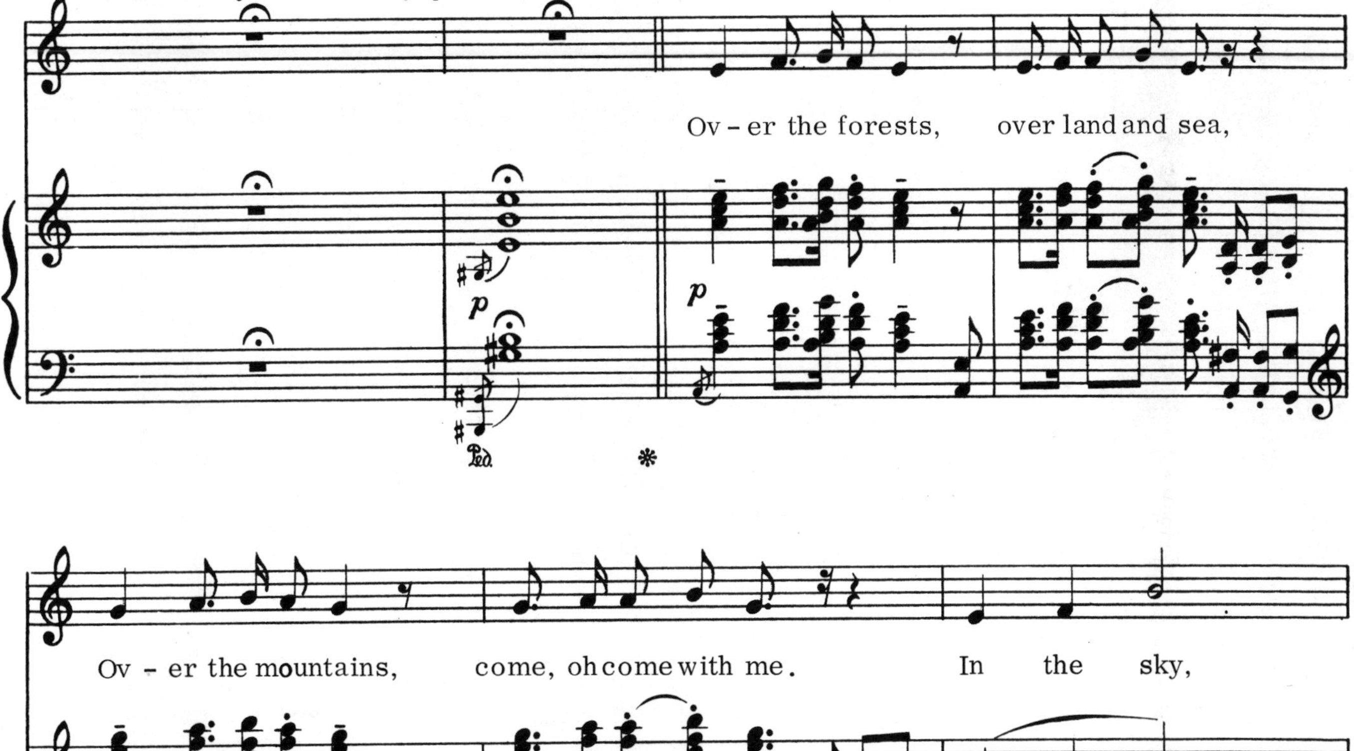

we will fly. Come with me to a land where heart and mind are
poco rit.

Più lento
free. Together we will dwell, — And all will yet be
p
p
p

well. — Come! Under my magic art all love will desert your heart.
p
p
cresc.

Come! A life of hap-pi-ness Un - der my spell. —
poco rit.

Allegro molto moderato
O - ver the forests, o - ver land and sea,
p
O - ver the mountains, come, oh come with me. In the sky,
we will fly. Come with me to a land where heart and mind are
3
poco rit.
free.
8
loco
f
a tempo
Ped
*

Segue No. 8

8. THE FLOWER GARDEN

(SOLDIERS AND FLOWERS)

1st Soldier
gar - den. Come and see, come and see, come and see. May
2nd Soldier
I present the Buttercups and Hya - cinths? Con - vol - vu - lus and Tiger Li - lies
1st Soldier
2nd Soldier
gay. Nar - cis-sus stand so proudly, here are Snow-drops. Look a -
-round you. We'll be glad for you to stay.

2
poco tranquillo
Flowers: Do stay and talk, How bored we are.
Buttercups: Do stay and talk, (Hyacinths): How bored we are. (Convolvulus):

Wish we could walk, Not be a flower.
Wish we could walk, (Tiger Lilies): Not be a flower.

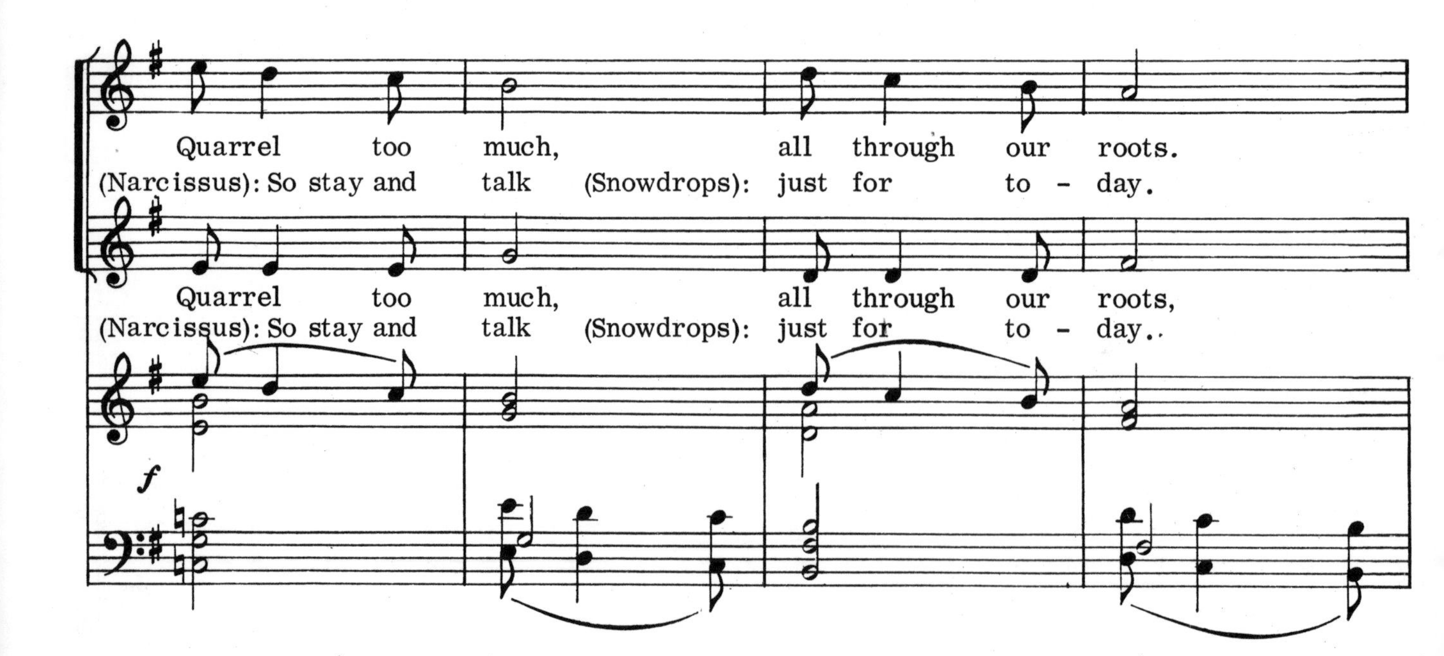
Quarrel too much, all through our roots.
(Narcissus): So stay and talk (Snowdrops): just for to - day.
Quarrel too much, all through our roots,
(Narcissus): So stay and talk (Snowdrops): just for to - day..
f

If we all could put on some boots.
(All): We beg you please, don't go a - way
If we all could put on some boots.
(All): We beg you please, don't go a - way.
3
Tempo I
Flowers & Soldiers
Do come and see the marvels of the
mp
gar - den. Follow me, follow me, follow me. It
really is a ver-y pretty gar - den, Come and see, come and see, come and

Soldiers
Flowers
Soldiers
see. It's wonder-ful, It's wonder-ful. Oh, do stay and talk! It's
see. It's wonder-ful, It's wonder-ful. Oh, do stay and talk! It's
Flowers
won-der-ful, It's won-der-ful. Oh, do stay and talk!
won-der-ful, It's won-der-ful. Oh, do stay and talk!
All
Do stay and talk! It's won-derful, won-derful, won-derful. Ah!
Do stay and talk! It's won-derful, won-derful, won-derful. Ah!
Dialogue

CUE. Gerda: "Thank you. Then I must ask the other flowers".

9. FLOWER SONG

(GERDA AND FLOWERS)

2 Allegretto
Gerda (spoken): "I don't understand". Tigerlilies: "We sing of what we know". Gerda:
Do you
p
mp
know where Karl has gone?
Convolvulus:
A
3
love - ly maiden stands a - lone. She leans up - on a tower of stone, And
waits, and sighs: "Will he not come? A - las and lack - a - day".

Gerda (spoken): "Do you mean Karl?" Convolvulus: "The story of our dream". Gerda:
Do you
p
mp
4
know where Karl has gone?
mf
5 Allegro moderato
Snowdrops:
Two little girls on a swing are swing-ing. Up on high they swing, as they
mp
swing they are sing - ing. Down on the ground is a lit - tle dog bark - ing,

Fro-lick-ing and jump-ing to join in the lark - ing.
Two lit-tle girls on a swing are swing-ing. Up on high they sing, as they
Gerda (spoken): "It's all very nice, but what about Karl?"
Snowdrops: "That is our story". Gerda:
sing they are swinging.
Do you
a tempo
p
poco rit.
6 Allegretto
know where Karl has gone?

7 Valse lento
Hyacinths:
Three love-ly mai - dens dance by the lake.
Three love-ly mai - dens dance by the lake.
mp cantabile
Sad - ly, so sad - ly they move to their graves.
Sad - ly, so sad - ly they move to their graves.
Each one must give and each one must take,
Each one must give and each one must take,

And then they sink 'neath the bil - low - ing waves.
And then they sink 'neath the bil - low - ing waves.

8
Gerda (spoken): "Very sad, I'm sure; but what about Karl?" Hyacinths: "We sing our song,

the only one we know". Gerda:
Do you know where Karl has gone?
mp

9 Allegretto espressivo
Buttercups:
An old, old wo-man sits at rest, Her
An old, old wo-man sits at rest, Her
rit. mp
grand-daughter comes to call, — And kis-ses her, and then at once,
grand-daughter comes to call, — And kis-ses her, and then at once,
cresc.
mf
p
Gold is o - ver all, — Like a shimmer-ing shawl, —
Gold is o - ver all, — Like a shimmer-ing shawl, —
cresc.
pp

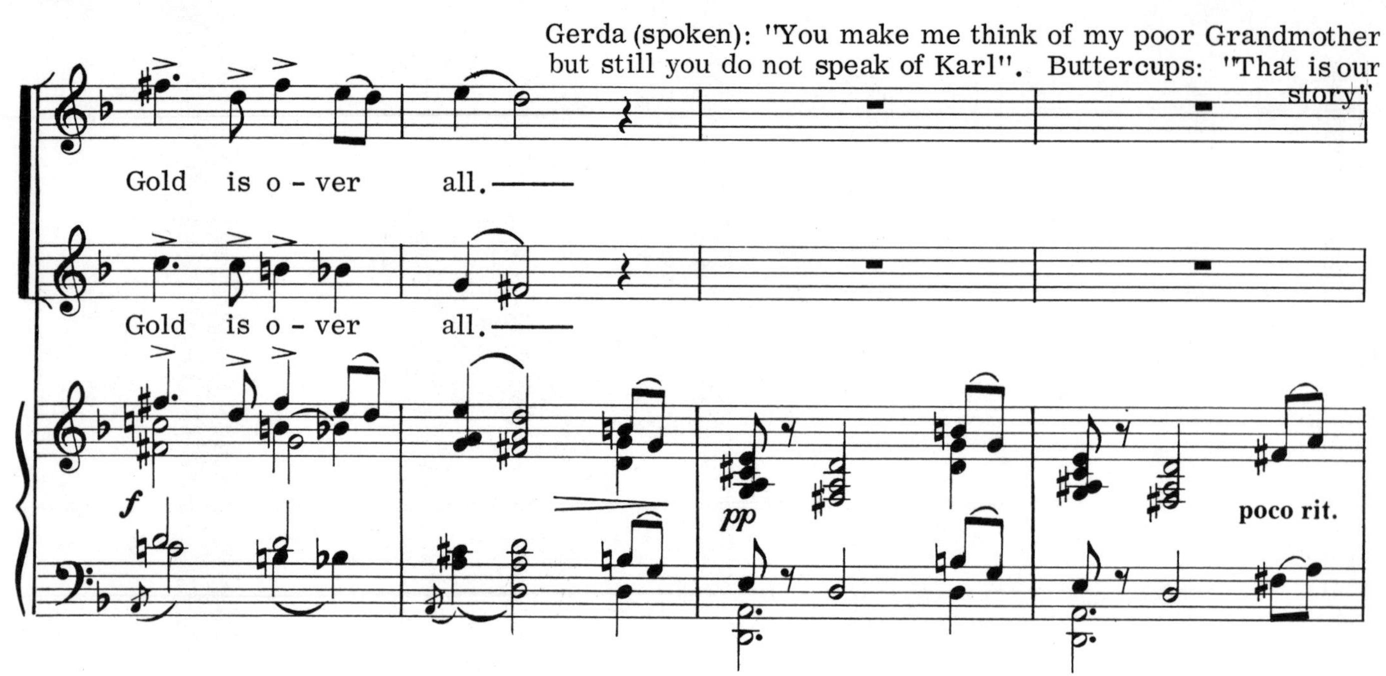
Gerda (spoken): "You make me think of my poor Grandmother but still you do not speak of Karl". Buttercups: "That is our story"
Gold is o - ver all.
Gold is o - ver all.
f
pp
poco rit.

Gerda:
10
Do you know where Karl has gone?
a tempo
mp

11
Allegro
Narcissus:
We can see our - selves when it rains, In pools of sil - ver - y light - ness.
mp

Oh, how beau - ti - ful we are, All de - li-ca-cy and bright - ness.

12 Allegretto grazioso
All flowers:
So we spend the day - light
So we spend the day - light
p
mp

telling all we know, But we've heard it all before, we
telling all we know, But we've heard it all before, we

wish that we could go. To learn a-no-ther stor - y; Sing a-no-ther
wish that we could go. To learn a-no-ther stor - y; Sing a-no-ther
song. If you think that life is hap - py here, you're ver - y
song. If you think that life is hap - py here, you're ver - y
poco rit.
wrong.
wrong.
p a tempo
cresc.
f
Dialogue

CUE. 1st Crow: "Come along, we've a long way to go, and you can't fly".

10. DANCE (SARABANDE)

(COURTIERS)

Andante non troppo

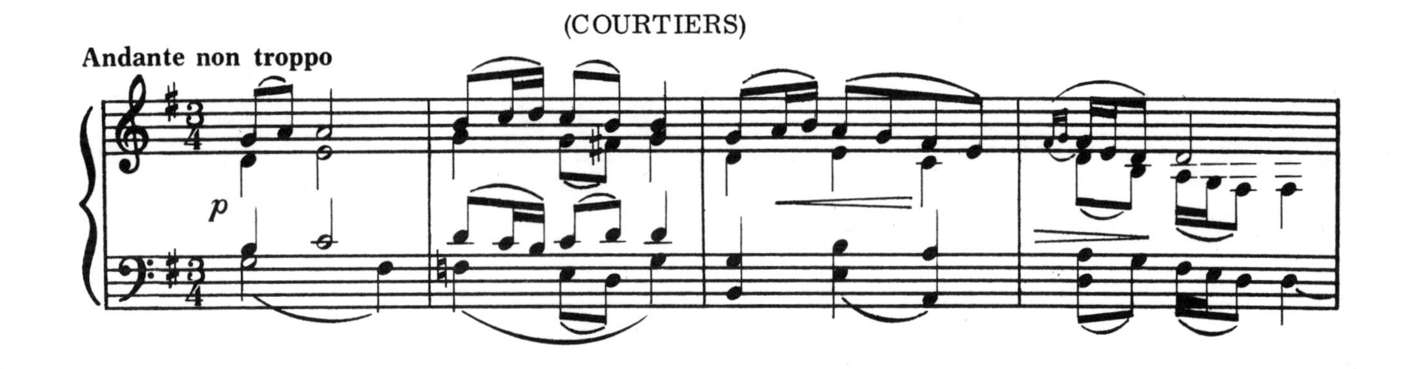

2
p

p

cresc.
3
f

p

cresc.
f poco rit.
p

CUE. Prince (kissing Princess' hand): "And we shall live happily ever after". Princess: "For ever".

11. FOR EVER

(PRINCE, PRINCESS AND CHORUS)

ther. To hold you, en - fold you, and ne - ver to part. A

f

hus - band and wife - time, For all our life - time, For ev - er

p

Chorus:

in my heart. For

2

ev - er, for ev - er, for - ev - er, A love to last a

life - time through. For ev - er, for ev - er, for ev -
life - time through. For ev - er, for ev - er, for ev -
- er, She'll keep her love for you.
3
Prince & Princess:
- er, She'll keep her love for you. To - ge -
- ther, to - ge - ther. To hold you, en - fold you, and ne - ver to
f

All:
A hus-band and wife-time, For all our their life-time, For
part. A hus-band and wife-time, For all our their life-time, For
ev - er in my your heart.
ev - er in my your heart.
p
4 (Music continues until Gerda calls "Karl")
poco rit.
mp
1
2

Dialogue

CUE. 2nd Crow: "Indeed, it will be most satisfactory".

12. CROWS IN CLOVER

Both:
And it's through assis - ting someone who was all a-lone. You'll find it's worth persisting
Now they'll lay the ta - ble spe-ci-ally for you and me. At last we will be a - ble to
poco ritard.

1
e-ven on your own.
live in lux-ur - y.
D.C.
DANCE a tempo
mf

Dialogue

CUE. Prince: "You will find him, Good-bye".

13. REPRISE FOR EVER

(PRINCE, PRINCESS AND CHORUS)

Gerda: "good-bye, your Highnesses". (she curtseys) "And my love and thanks to you both". Crows: "We'll come to the edge of the forest with you".

through. For ev - er, for ev - er, for ev - er, She'll keep her
I'll my
through. For ev - er, for ev - er, for ev - er, She'll keep her
I'll my
2
love for you. To - ge - ther, to - ge -
love for you. To - ge - ther, to - ge -
- ther. To hold you, en - fold you, and ne-ver to part. A husband and
- ther. To hold you, en - fold you, and ne-ver to part. A husband and
f

wife-time, For all our their life-time, For ev - er in my her heart.
wife-time, For all our their life-time, For ev - er in my her heart.
p
3
For ev - er in my heart.
For ev - er in my heart.
f
(CURTAIN)
END OF ACT ONE

ACT TWO

14. WE RIDE OVER THE MOUNTAINS

(ROBBER KING AND ROBBER BAND)

Robber Women:
Watching, waiting and hoping;
Is there a traveller finding his way?
Is there a traveller finding his way?
2 Robber King:
Più mosso
Then out of the night We move
into the fight, And swords flash in the

dark, And knives make for their mark.

All:
Then tri - umph comes fast; the dan - ger is past.
poco rit.

3
Robber Men:
We ride over the moun - tains,
p
f
a tempo

Deep in the fo - rests, seek-ing our prey.

Robber Women
Watch - ing, wait-ing and ho - ping; Is there a tra - veller
Watch - ing, wait-ing and ho - ping; Is there a tra - veller
finding his way? Finding his way?
finding his way? Finding his way?
Finding his way?
Finding his way?

Dialogue

CUE. Robber King: "Gladly. Come, we'll all go."

Is there a tra - veller find-ing his way?
Is there a tra - veller find-ing his way?
Find-ing his way? Find-ing his
Find-ing his way? Finding his
way?
way?

Dialogue

CUE. Robber Girl: "He'll take his time".

16. FAR AWAY

(REINDEER, GERDA AND ROBBER GIRL)

Reindeer:
Far a - way, far —— a - way. ——
that's where you'll

find Karl at play. ——
I saw her

Gerda:
fly - ing a - long; I heard her i - cy song, Can it be true?

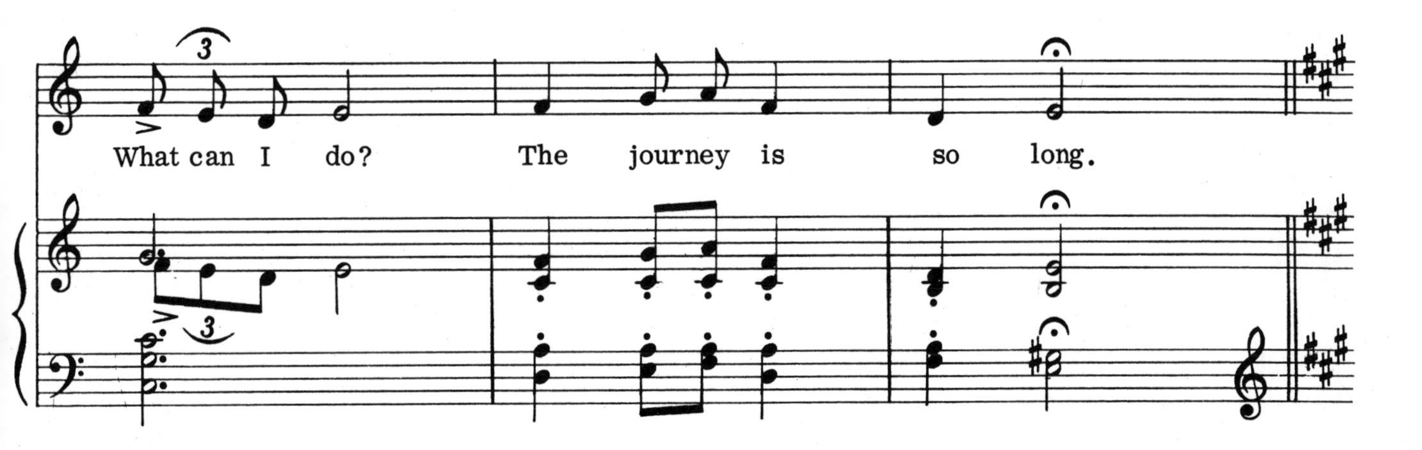
What can I do? The journey is so long.

2
Reindeer:
Ah, the Snow Queen, beau - ti-ful Snow Queen, Gli - ding se -
p

rene - ly ov - er—the— white waste. Ah, the
rit.
a tempo

Snow Queen, beau - ti - ful Snow Queen Off to her

3
pa - lace You must make haste.
f
mp

Robber Girl
Far a - way, far a - way,

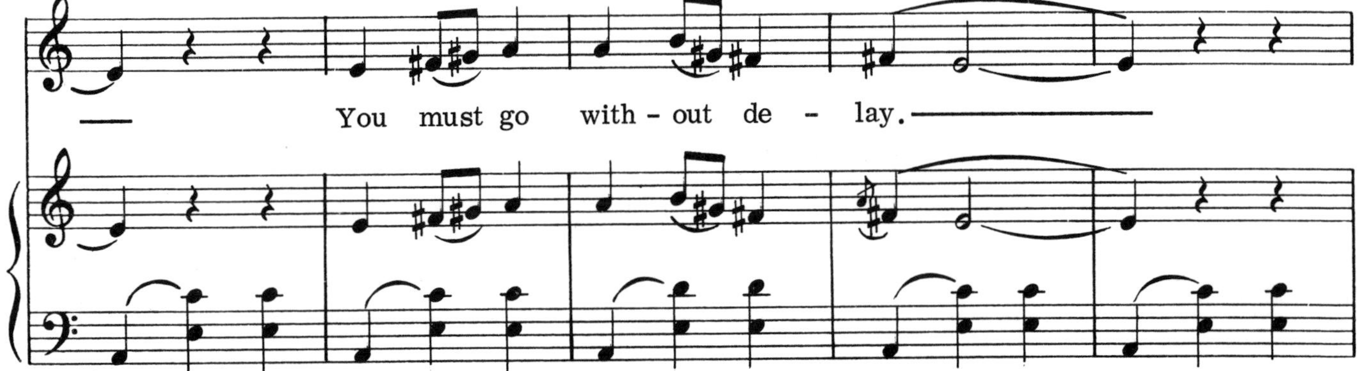
You must go with - out de - lay.

Up - on his back you may ride; I'll let him go from my side.
3

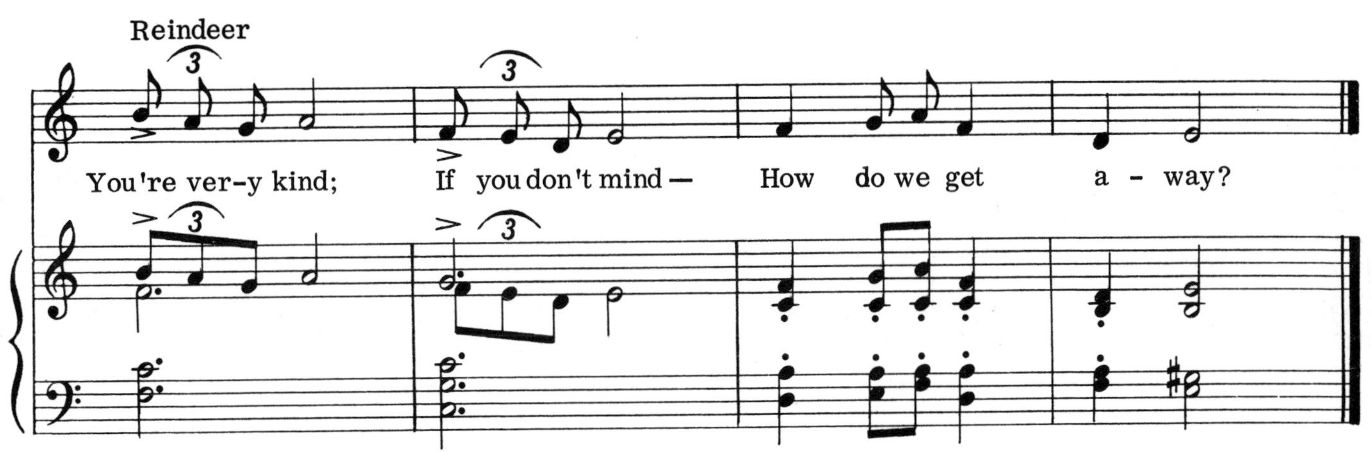
Reindeer
You're ver-y kind; If you don't mind — How do we get a - way?
3

Dialogue

CUE. Reindeer: "One day you'll hurt somebody with that, silly girl".

17. REPRISE WE RIDE OVER THE MOUNTAINS

Allegretto (ROBBER KING AND ROBBER BAND offstage)

p

We ride —— o-ver the

moun - tains, —— Deep in the fo - rests, —— seek-ing our

Is there a tra - veller find-ing his
Is there a tra - veller find-ing his
way? Find - ing his way?
way? Find - ing his way?
Find-ing his way?
Find-ing his way?

Dialogue

CUE. Robber King: "Goodnight, old woman."

18. REPRISE WE RIDE OVER THE MOUNTAINS

Dialogue

CUE. Gerda: "Farewell, good friend."

19. FISH

(FINNISH WOMAN)

meat is scarce, So I live on fish a-lone; it couldn't be much worse.
2
Come on, lit - tle fish - es;
Make the best of what we've got, And I'll eat the sca - ly lot; oh
cresc.
how I hate these fish - es.
sf
Dialogue

CUE; Finnish Woman: "Sit down and listen."

20. INNOCENCE

(FINNISH WOMAN)

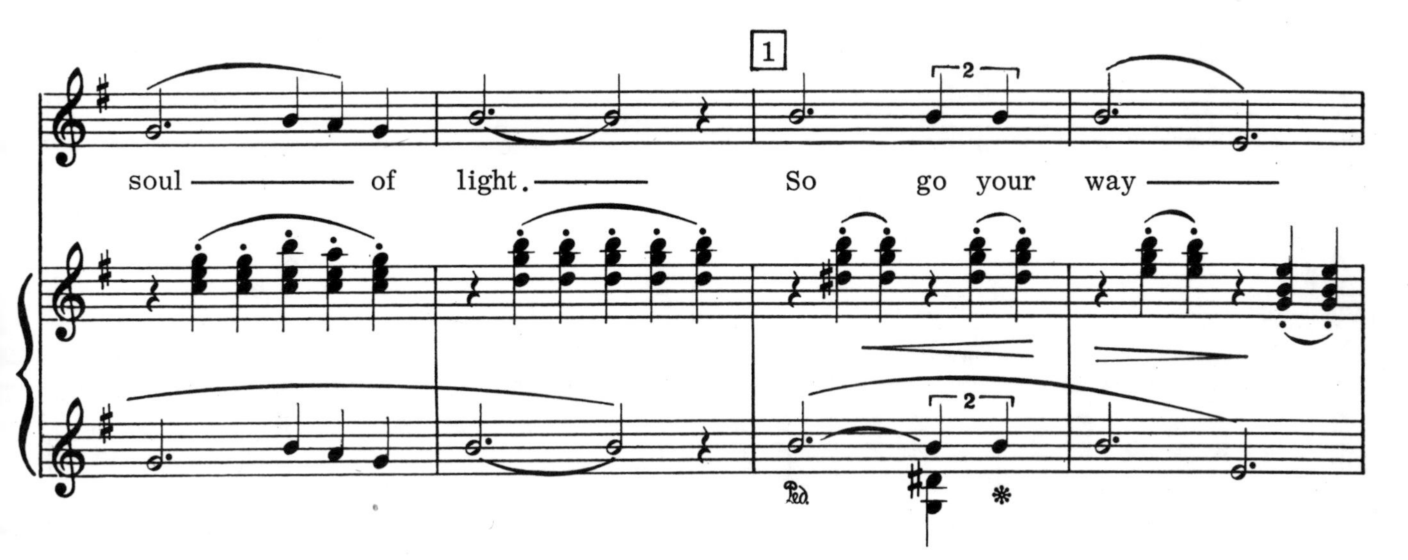

now you've come so far. Nought —— can stop you,
fz molto rit.
p a tempo
2
2

armed as you are. Not all her ma - gic can keep you a -
cresc.
2
2

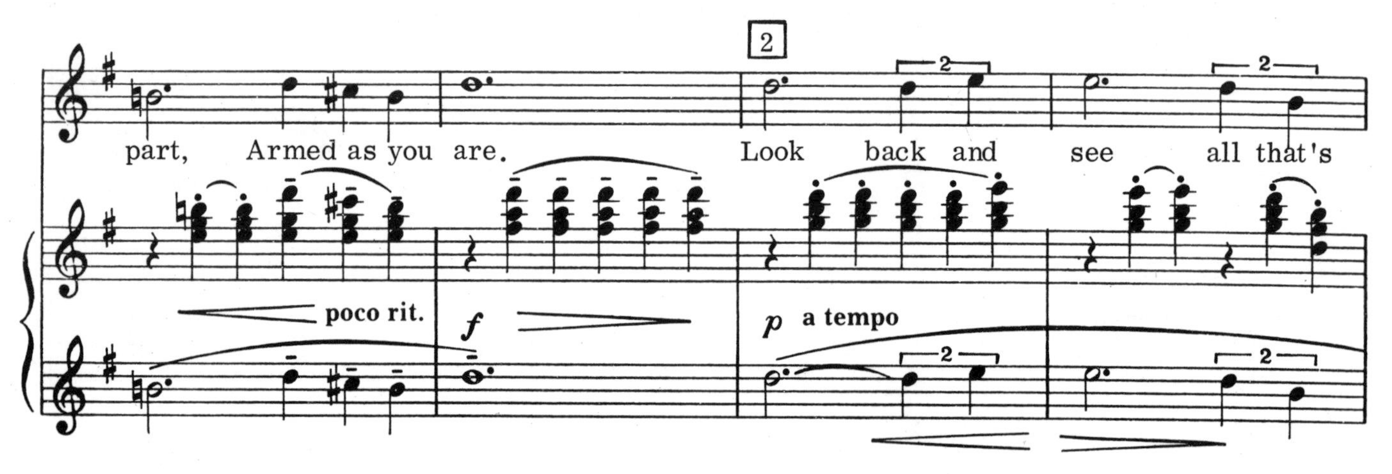
2
part, Armed as you are. Look back and see all that's
poco rit.
f
p a tempo
2
2

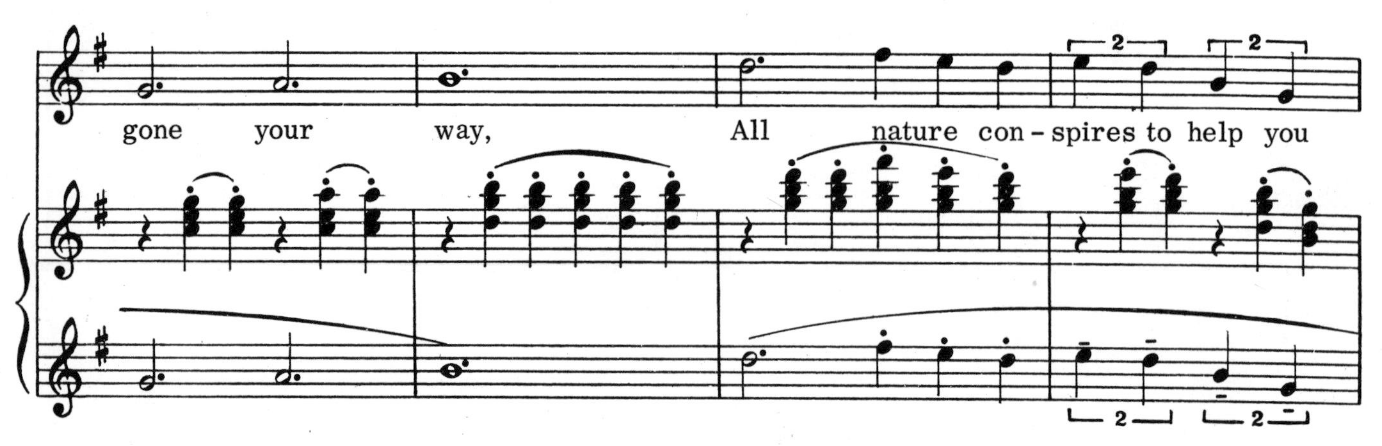
gone your way, All nature con - spires to help you
2
2

3
day by day. Keep innocence of
Ped

heart ever green. Let the truth o-ver-
Ped

4
throw the Snow Queen. Let the wea - pon of truth o-ver
cresc.
f

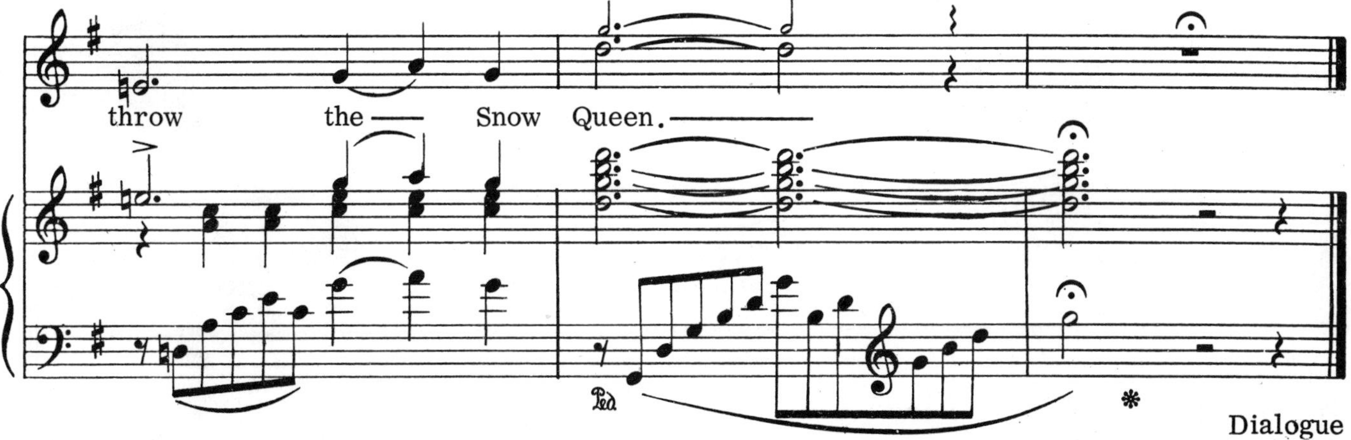
throw the Snow Queen.
Ped

Dialogue

CUE. Finnish Woman: "Wait, wait, your boots, your coat" (curtains close)

21. BALLET OF SNOWFLAKES (OPTIONAL)

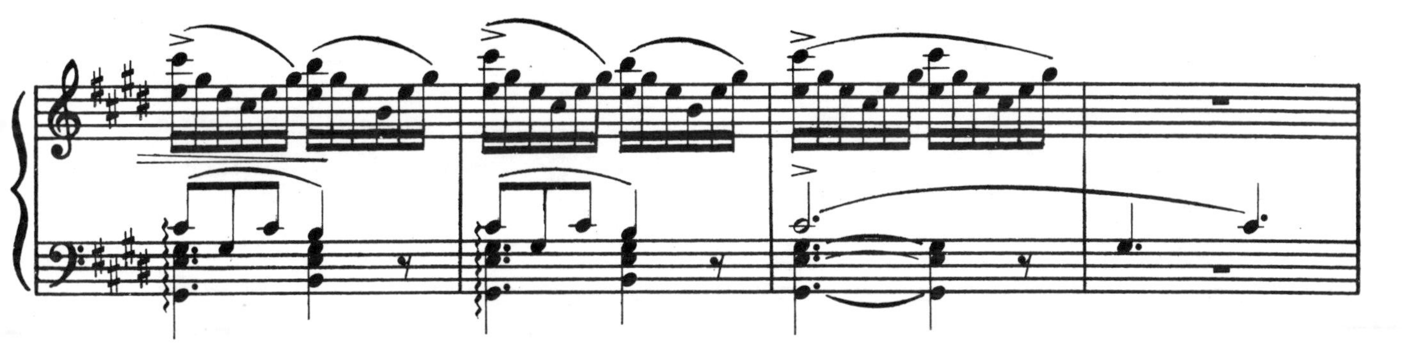

3
Tranquillo
pp
tr

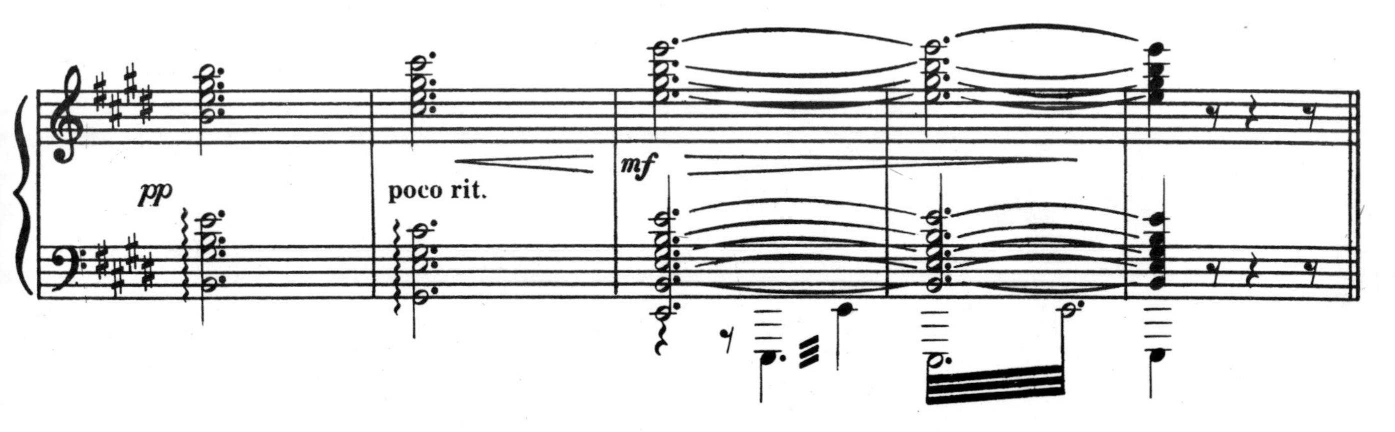
pp
poco rit.
mf

-2-

Allegro grazioso

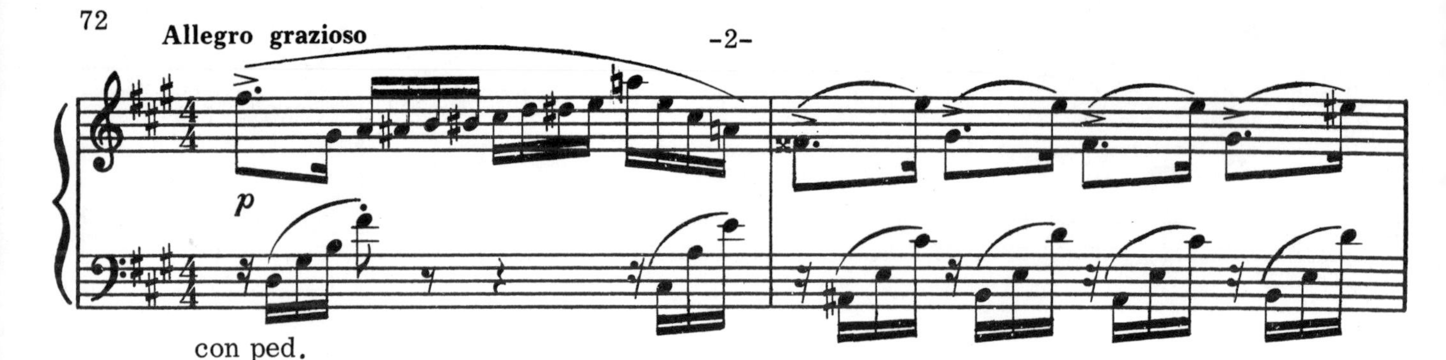

pp

pp
rit.

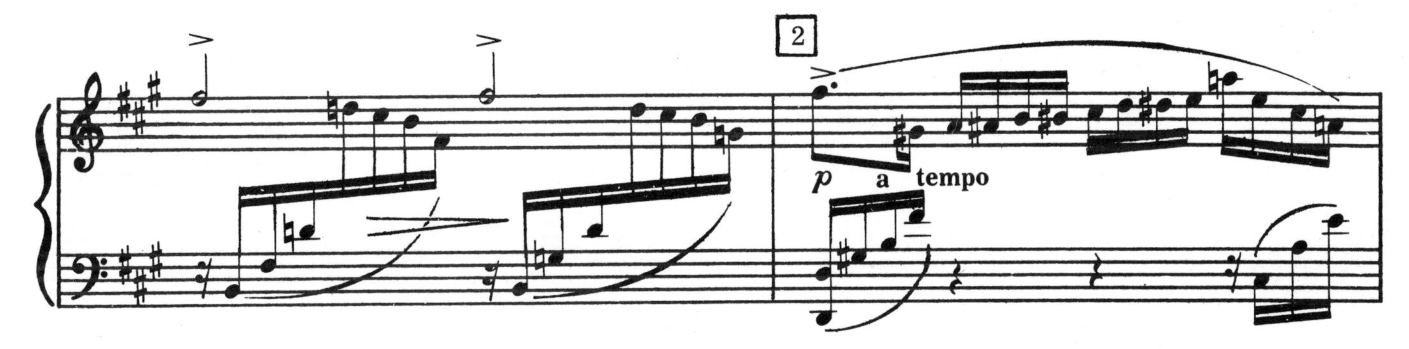
2
p a tempo

cresc.

f

ffz

dim. e rit.
p
pp

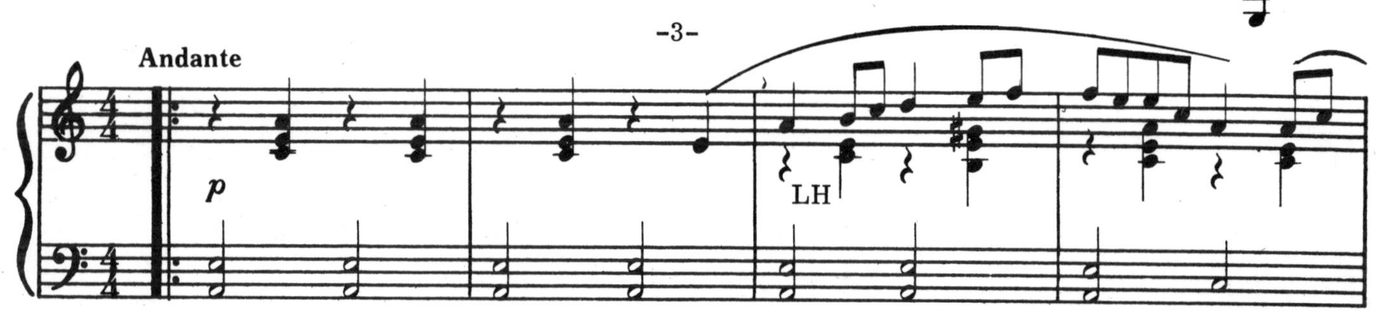
-3-
Andante
p
LH

mf

1
p

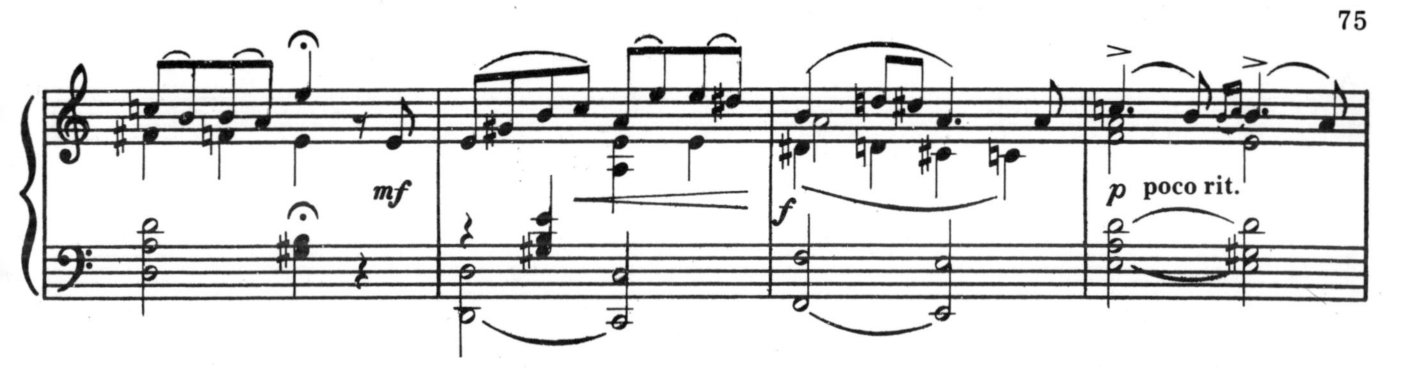
mf
f
p poco rit.

2 Allegretto
pp

mf
p

rit.
pp

 Molto allegro e sempre staccato

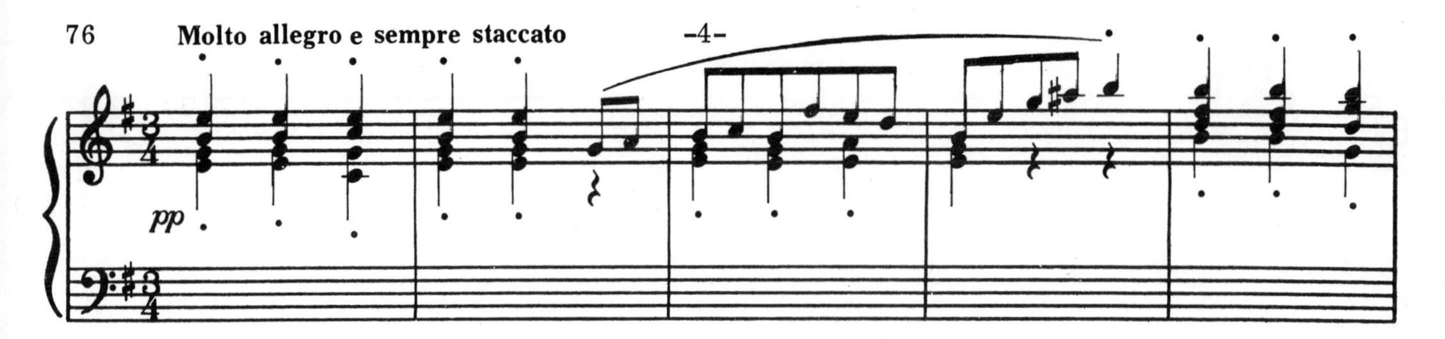

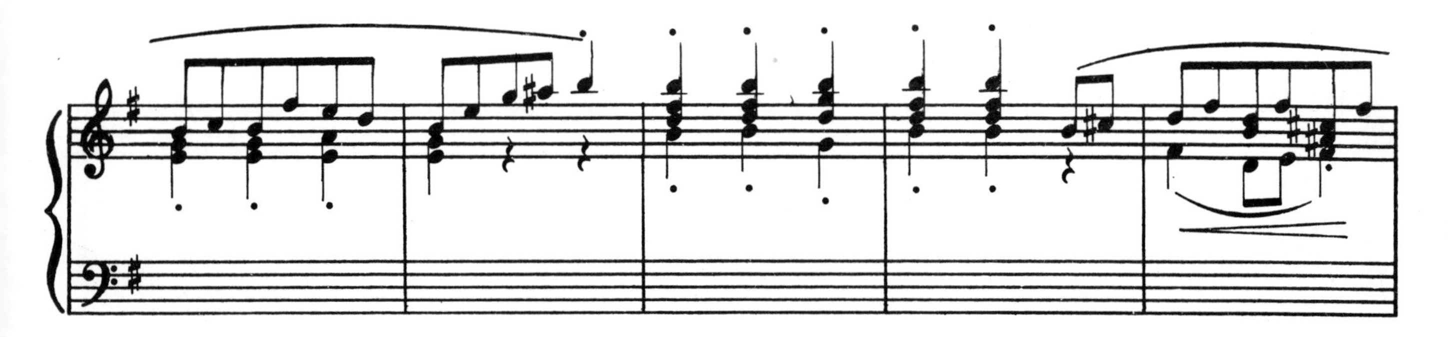

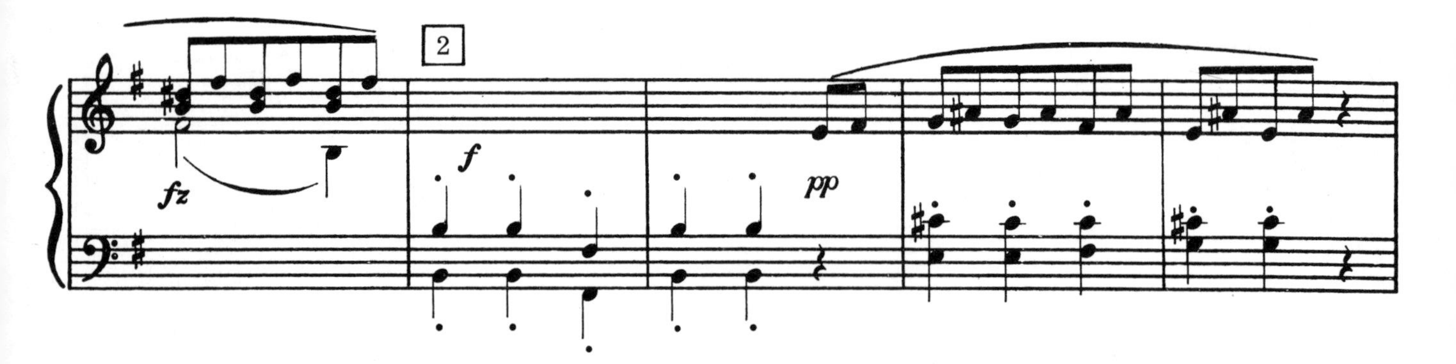

Dialogue

CUE. Karl: "I'm not unhappy about it, though, it's just that – "

2
words I can-not get. Words like "hea - ven","pure", and "love" seem
well be - yond my mind. Where is my e - ter - ni - ty? When
will I seek and find?
3 Snow Queen. "But you say that you are not
unhappy. You like it here?" Karl."Yes, I like it, and I like you. But it's all very puzzling".

Snow Queen. "There's no puzzle; —— listen:"
mf
4 Snow Queen
Words must have a mean - ing clear, Both strong and full of sense.
Clar - i - ty will ban - ish fear, And ne - ver give of - fence.
5
Pay at - ten - tion to the mind; Look at things with ea - gle eyes.

Cold - ly an - a - lyse and find There's more to- life than sighs.
6
Rea - son rules this world of mine, Though ic - y it may seem.
There-fore let cold rea-son shine, And you'll for - get to dream.
You'll for - get to dream.

Dialogue

CUE. Snow Queen: "Goodbye, I shall not be long away."

23. REPRISE WINTER

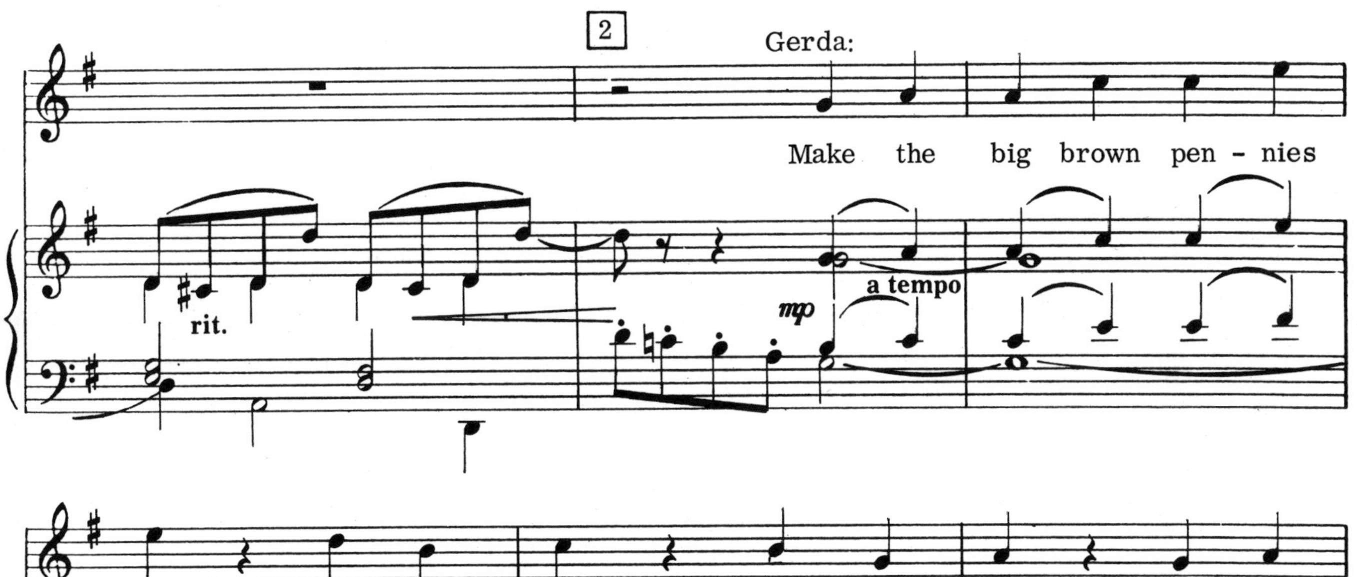
2
Gerda:
Make the big brown pen - nies
rit.
mp
a tempo

hot. Take one up, find a spot On the

fros - ty win - dow pane---
fz
pp

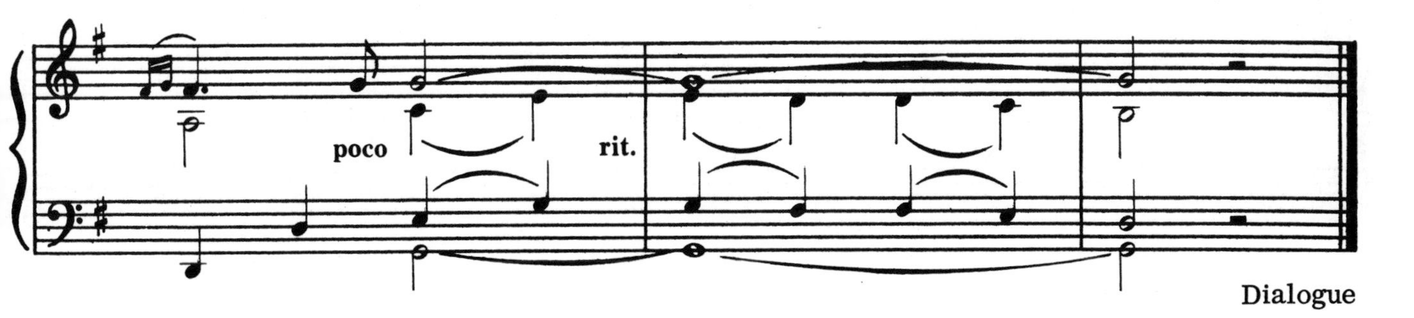
poco
rit.

Dialogue

CUE. Gerda: "Home again?" Karl: "Home."

24. HOME

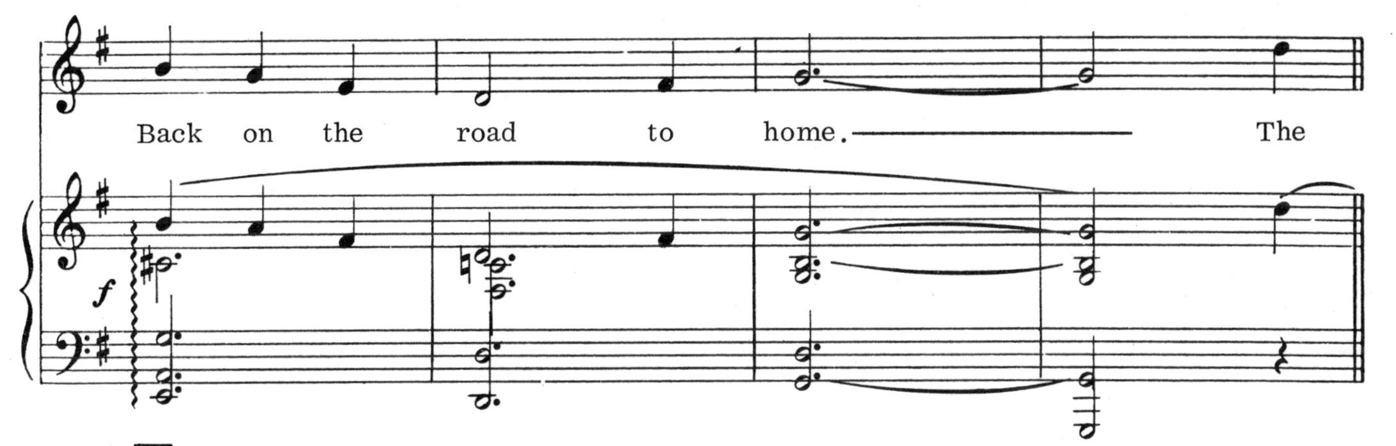

Back on the road to home. The
f

2
way may be lone - ly, the road may be long. It's

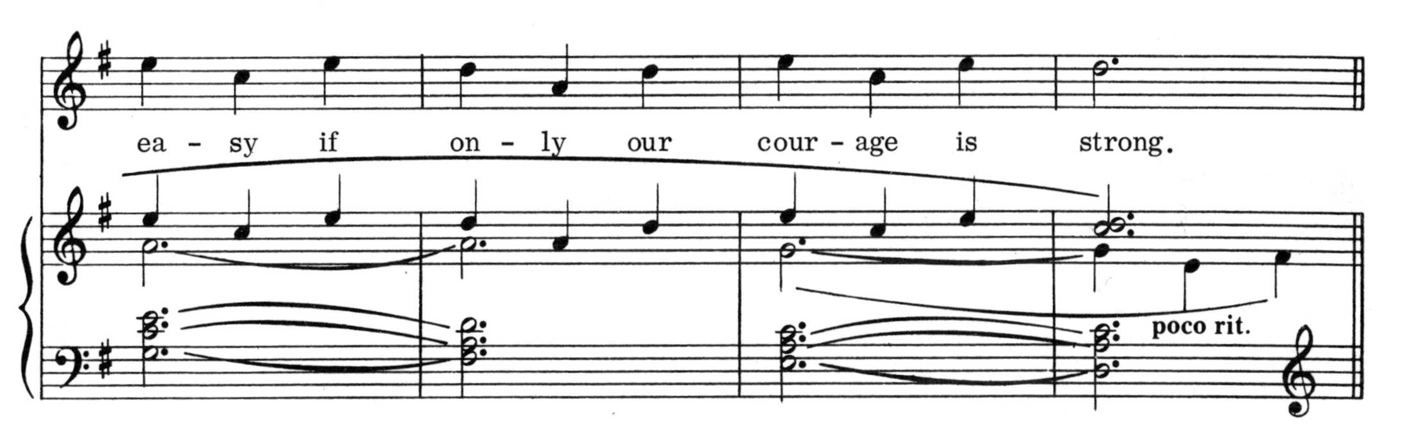

ea - sy if on - ly our cour - age is strong.
poco rit.

3
Hand in hand to the Spring we will go,
a tempo

Out of the ice, out of the snow.
Hand in hand all the way we will roam,
cresc.
Back on the road to home.
f
4
Allegretto moderato (repeat if required)
mp
Segue No. 25

25. ONE THAT GOT AWAY
(HOBGOBLIN)
5 Allegro moderato
Hobgoblin:
mf
How I hate some - one to get a -
way from what I've planned.
How I hate the bird to fly that
I had in my hand.
6
Gone is all I
wait - ed for,
Hat - ed for;

What is more:

7
Ug - li - ness has turned to beau - ty, that is worst of all.

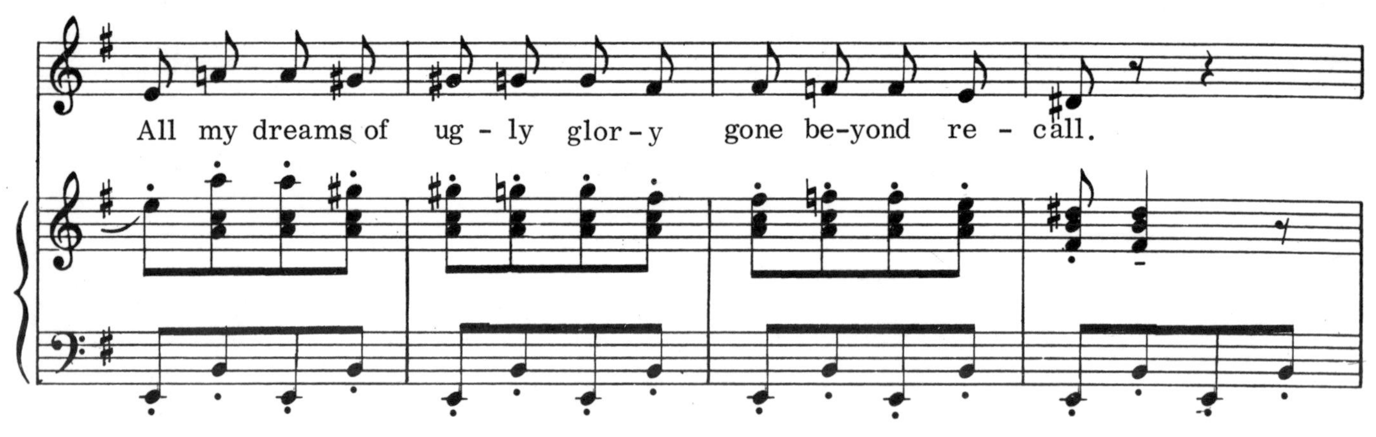
All my dreams of ug - ly glor - y gone be-yond re - call.

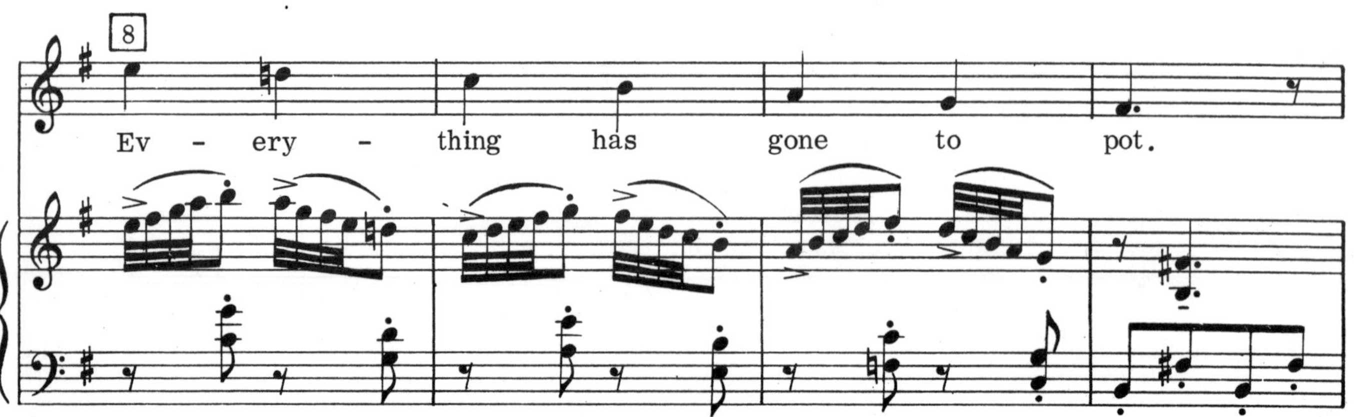
8
Ev - ery - thing has gone to pot.

Ev - ery - thing that I've got. That's

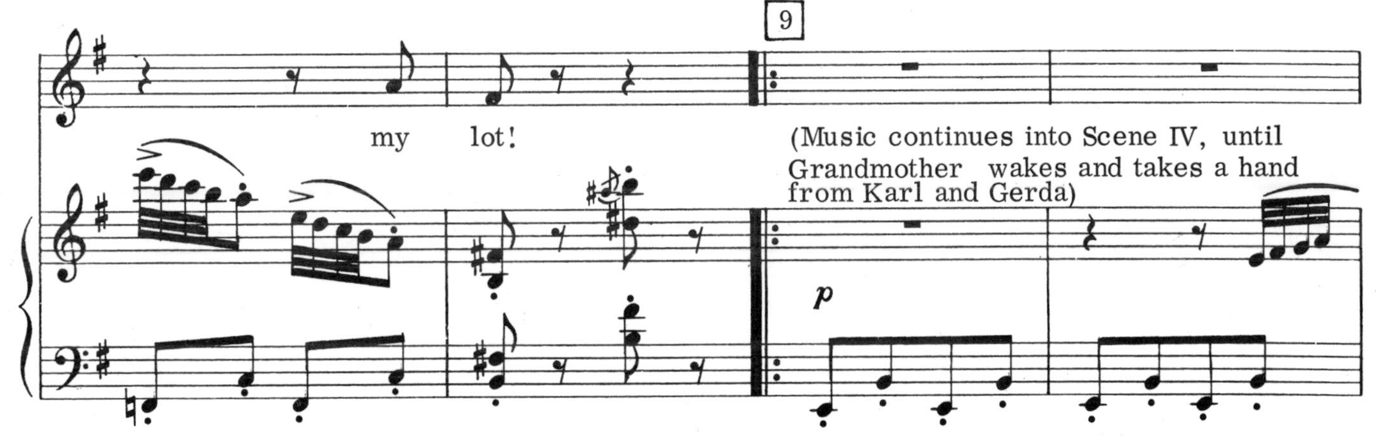
9
my lot!
(Music continues into Scene IV, until Grandmother wakes and takes a hand from Karl and Gerda)
p

Dialogue

CUE. Grandmother: "And what of the Snow Queen!" Karl & Gerda: "Who?"

(KARL, GERDA, GRANDMOTHER AND CHILDREN)

Hand in hand all the way we will roam,
cresc.
Back on the road to home. The
f
2
way may be lone - ly, the road may be long, It's
ea - sy if on - ly our cour - age is strong.

3
Gerda and Children:
Hand in hand we will tra - vel a -
Karl and Grandmother:
Ah!
ff
rit.
ff a tempo
- long, Sing - ing a song, sing - ing a song.
Sing - ing a song, sing - ing a song.
Hand in hand all the way we will roam, Back on the
Ah! Back on the

4
road to home. Back home. Back
road to home. Back home. Back
home.
home.
ff
(curtain)
rit.
sfz
END OF ACT TWO